BRER RABBIT AND HIS TRICKS

DRAWINGS BY EDWARD GOREY

YOUNG SCOTT BOOKS
NEW YORK

ENNIS REES

Library of Congress Catalog Card No. 67-21800
Text © 1967 by Ennis Rees
Illustrations © 1967 by Edward Gorey
All rights reserved. Printed in U.S.A.

NOTE

For many years, people in the American South have told stories about Brer Rabbit, dozens and dozens of them. Some children in the South, long before they learn to read, still hear these stories from adults. But fewer and fewer people seem to know them nowadays, mostly because of the difficult dialect in which they were originally recorded. This is a pity, for the Brer Rabbit stories are among the best folktales we have.

Since the language of the original Southern versions has all the wit and richness of good poetry, I have here selected three of my favorite Brer Rabbit stories and attempted to re-create them in rhyming verse. Of course I hope these story poems in modern English will be enjoyed for themselves, but if they also serve to lead the reader on to older collections of dialect tales about Brer Rabbit, so much the better.

Versions of many of these stories have been told all over the world in many different languages for countless generations, but especially in Africa. And Brer Rabbit is what students of folklore call a "trickster." There are many tricksters in the stories of different peoples from Asia and Africa to America. Sometimes they take the form of a man, but often that of a spider, a raven, a coyote, or some other creature. For us Brer Rabbit is the funniest and most effective trickster of all, and he remains our best example of how the small and weak can often outwit and thereby triumph over the large and powerful and hungry. But not always. Once in awhile, Brer Rabbit is too smart for his own good, and so gets the worst of it.

In the stories, Brer Rabbit's other name is Riley, and his children are sometimes called "the little Rabs," for short.

ENNIS REES
Columbia, S.C.

14319

BRER RABBIT and the TAR BABY

Old Mr. Fox had long had enough
Of tricky Brer Rabbit's treating him rough.
So he went to work and mixed a big jar
Of turpentine and sticky-stick tar,
From which remarkable mixture he made
Something to put other traps in the shade.

He was out for revenge and he didn't mean maybe,
And what he had made he called a Tar Baby.
  He took it out to the road into town
And there he set the Tar Baby down.
Then, having rid himself of his load,
He hid in the bushes beside the big road—
And just in time, for hoppity-hippity,
Here came Brer Rabbit, lippity-clippity,
Sassy as any jay-bird in the world.
But even Brer Rabbit's eyeballs twirled
When he saw the Baby of Brer Fox's plot.

Now Riley Rabbit was certainly not
The sort of creature that sits up and begs,
But there he sat back upon his hind legs
And said to the Tar Baby, trying to coax,
"Good morning to you. How're all of your folks?"
    Then, when the Tar Baby didn't reply,
Brer Rabbit raised his voice up high
And said, "Hello there! Good morning, I say.
It sure is nice weather we're having today."
But the Baby just sat as a Tar Baby does,
And old Mr. Fox lay low where he was.

"You deaf?" said Brer Rabbit. "Because if you are
I can yell a lot louder than I have so far!"
But the Baby just sat as a Tar Baby does,
And old Mr. Fox lay low where he was.

  "I know your trouble," Brer Rabbit said.
"*You* are stuck-up and you've got a big head.
Well I'm just the one to cure you of that.
Now if you don't hurry and take off your hat
And say good morning to me like you should,
I'm going to draw back and wallop you good!"

At this old Brer Fox peeped out through the bushes
And chuckled a little down back of his tushes.
Brer Rabbit kept yelling, asking and asking,
But Tar Baby he just sat there a-basking.
At last Brer Rabbit drew back and blip!
He hit the Tar Baby smack on the lip.
And there Brer Rabbit got stuck up too.
This creature he'd found was as sticky as glue.
But the Baby just sat as a Tar Baby does,
And old Mr. Fox lay low where he was.

"If you don't let me go, I'll whop you again!"
Said Riley, then hit him right square on the chin.
And that fist stuck as the other one had,
And now Brer Rabbit was sure feeling bad.
"Turn me loose! Turn me loose!" he said with a shout,
"Before I kick all of your stuffing out!"
And so he kicked, still shouting demands,
Till both of his feet were stuck like his hands.
But the Baby just sat as a Tar Baby does,
And old Mr. Fox lay low where he was.
    And Brer Rabbit squealed and squabbled and squalled
And struggled and grunted and cussed and called,
Saying that if he wouldn't turn loose
He'd butt the Tar Baby, but what was the use—
He'd no sooner butted than there Riley's head
Got stuck like the rest, and was his face red!

For just about then out sauntered Brer Fox,
Innocent-looking and kicking at rocks.
"Why howdy, Brer Rabbit," he said, half yawning,
"You seem to be sort of stuck-up this morning."

With that he laughed until he was sore,
Then rolled on the ground and laughed some more.
At last, when Brer Fox had got back his breath,
He said, "Well, Brer Rabbit, I'm tickled to death
To see the close friendship that you have struck up
With my Tar Baby there, but since you are *stuck* up
With tar in your hair, I've come here to haunt you.
I've got you this time right where I want you!

You just stick around, Brer Rabbit, and hush,
While I light up a big pile of brush,
So I can have rabbit barbecue,
And with what's left over I'll make rabbit stew!"
   To this Brer Rabbit, as best he could,
Said, "I don't care if you burn me with wood,
Brer Fox—I'll even lend you a match.
But please don't fling me in that briar patch!"

"A fire's too much trouble and has to be fed,"
Said Brer Fox—"I think I'll hang you instead."
"Hang me as high as ever you please,"
Brer Rabbit replied, "I'll swing in the breeze.
Do what you want, Brer Fox, with your catch,
But please don't fling me in that briar patch!"

"Well since I don't have any cord to put roun' you
For hanging, I think I had better go drown you."
"Drown me, Brer Fox. Not a breath will I snatch.
But please don't fling me in that briar patch!"

"There's no water near," said Brer Fox. "I suppose
I'll have to skin you—let's start with your nose!"
"Go on and start, Brer Fox. Skin me good.
Snatch out my eyeballs, slush out my blood.
Tear out my ears and my hair by the batch,
But please don't fling me in that briar patch!"

Now old Brer Fox wanted badly to boast
That he had done that which hurt Riley most.
So he took him up by the two hind legs,
Saying, "I didn't know that Brer Rabbit begs,"
And then he flung him right into the middle
Of that briar patch, and grinning a little
He sat down to watch where he saw Riley fall.

But almost at once he heard someone call.
　　And then came one of the biggest shocks
That ever came to old Brer Fox.
For way up the hill, plain to see,
Was Riley himself, just as pert as could be,
Sitting up there on a chinkapin log
As happy as any frog in a bog,
Combing the tar from his hair with a chip,
Ready and waiting with one final quip:

"You see, Brer Fox, I don't have a scratch—
I was born and bred in the briar patch!"
And with that Brer Rabbit skipped away,
Spry as a cricket and twice as gay.

"HELLO, HOUSE!"

One time Brer Wolf got to thinking how he
Was as smart as Brer Rabbit, or ought to be,
And he made a plan to catch him at last
So all of his trick-playing days would be past.
He picked a day when the little Rabs dallied
Out in the meadow picking some salad
And old Mrs. Rabbit had finished her labors
And gone off to chat for a while with the neighbors.
Then Brer Wolf entered the house of Riley
And waited for him, oh ever so slyly.

But when Riley came up into the yard,
He looked at the house and he looked at it hard,
Because he noticed the door was cracked
And he knew it was a matter of fact
That he had never in all of his life
Seen it so left by the Rabs or his wife.
So Riley at once got mighty suspicious
That inside his house was somebody vicious.
Thought he, "I'm going to find out who's inside
Without going in and risking my hide.
There're more ways of telling who fell in the drink
Than falling in there yourself, I think."

Now anybody who went in at once
Would soon have been something worse than a dunce,
For nothing would have been left of him there
But a scrap of hide and a handful of hair.
So Riley tiptoed around for a while,
Then very quickly changing his style
He went out front and with a small jump
He perched himself on top of a stump
And called out loudly, "Hello, House!"
The house was as quiet as little Miss Mouse,
And Brer Wolf inside didn't answer a word.
He just seemed to be puzzled by what he had heard.

Then Brer Rabbit hollered "Hello, House!" again,
And Brer Wolf was puzzled worse than he'd been.
Why Riley kept calling, Brer Wolf didn't know,
And when he yelled, "House, can't you say hello?"
Brer Wolf got so warm he started to itch
And then so nervous he started to twitch.
At last Riley hollered as loud as he could:
"Hey, House, you're worse than so much dead wood!
What is the matter with you? Are you mad?
Have you lost what little manners you had?"
At this Brer Wolf felt awfully alone
And like he'd been hit on the funny bone.

"Well I declare," Brer Rabbit said,
"That house acts just like it's sick, or dead,
Because until now whenever I've tried
To be friendly to it, it's always replied,
'Hello yourself, how're all of the folks?'"

Now Brer Wolf wasn't too good at jokes,
And when he heard that, he got shaky below
And the next time Riley shouted "Hello!"
Brer Wolf tried to sound as much as he could
Like he thought a talking rabbit house would
And he said, in a voice like a frog's when he croaks,
"Hello yourself, how're all of the folks?"

At this Riley winked at himself and said:
"What's the matter, House? Got a cold in the head?"
And then he sat back upon his rump
And laughed till he almost fell off the stump.
"Brer Wolf," he yelled, "that was not worth a dime.
You'll have to stand out in the rain a long time
Before you'll be able to talk half as hoarse
As that house can talk—to me, of course."

At that Brer Wolf came slinking out
For all the world like a low-down lout
And then made a break for home, very fast,
As if he expected a shotgun blast,

And after that Riley had more peace of mind
And was pestered less by Brer Wolf and his kind.

WINNIANIMUS GRASS *and* WHIPMEWHOPME CAKE

One long hard winter the little Rabs got
So hungry and thin that Riley was not
Above the borrowing of a few
Of Mr. Man's chickens, one or two—
At a time, that is—and after their ride
In Brer Rabbit's sack, they'd all have them fried.
And there wasn't much in those days of slim pickings
That those little Rabs preferred to fried chickens.

But what for the chickens was surely the finish
Did nothing to make the feathers diminish.
The feathers piled up, until Mrs. Bunny
Said, "This is too much, now, Riley, honey.
Do get these feathers out of here."
And Riley said that he had an idea.

So he stuffed the feathers into a big sack,
And slinging it lightly across his back
He started off down the road that led past
Brer Fox's house, and traveling fast
He got there soon, nor was he too late
To meet Brer Fox coming out of the gate.

Brer Fox said, "Good morning. Where are you going?"
At this Riley stopped, puffing and blowing,
And said, "Brer Fox, to the mill—perhaps,
That is to say, if I don't collapse.
This load I've got won't let me go fast
And I'm not sure how long I will last.
I'm not what I used to be, you know.
You may be real strong, Brer Fox—I hope so.
But as for myself, you needn't doubt it,
I'm on the downgrade, no two ways about it."
Then Riley sat down as if he were stiff
And wiped his face with his handkerchief.

Brer Fox said, "What's in the bag, Brer Rabbit?"
And came over to him just like he might grab it.
"I'll bet it's either some corn or some wheat
Or something else even better to eat."
"No," said Riley, looking all worn,
"It's sure not wheat and it's sure not corn.
It's just what I sell to Mr. Millver
Down there at the mill for gold and silver.
To tell what it is makes me feel right funny,
'Cause it's all I've got that's worth big money."

At this Brer Fox pricked up his ears,
But soon laid them back with a couple of sneers
Because Brer Rabbit wouldn't say
What he had in the sack that was worth so much pay.
He kept on begging Riley to tell him.
"What is it you've got that you're going to sell him?
What is it?" he asked, and asked and asked,
Just dying to know, until at long last
Brer Rabbit said, "Well, if you won't breathe a word
To anyone else about what you've heard,
I'll tell you what I've got in here.
It's queer stuff, Brer Fox, mighty queer!"

Brer Fox crossed his heart and hoped he would die
If he ever told so much as Brer Fly,
To which Riley said, "Brer Fox, you'll pass.
They call the stuff Winnianimus grass,
And after it's been to the mill and ground,
It's worth at least nine dollars a pound.
The folks who buy it use it to make
Something they call Whipmewhopme cake."

This made Brer Fox's eyes open wide
And lifting the sack, he said, "What's inside
Sure is a mighty light sort of stuffing.
I don't understand why you're panting and puffing."
"You know," said Brer Rabbit, "that very few are
As big and strong, Brer Fox, as you are.
It's heavy for me, and you can believe it—
A little bit more, and I'd have to leave it!"

At this Brer Fox saw a good chance to nab it,
So he said, "I'll carry it for you, Brer Rabbit,
As surely any old friend of yours should.
A little walk will do me good."
So planning to give Brer Rabbit the slip,
He carried the sack at a goodly clip
Till Riley looked back and saw Mr. Man

And said, "Brer Fox, I've gone all I can.
You're just too much for me, I'll swear.
You go on ahead and I'll meet you there."
Grinning, Brer Fox said that he would bet
He could go twice as fast as he had gone yet,
And off he took, with visions, alas,
Of what he would get for that very strange grass.

Pretty soon Mr. Man came along and said,
"Who's that I see with the bag up ahead,
And do you know what's in it, Brer Rabbit?"
At this Riley answered that he shouldn't blab it,
But that was Brer Fox, and although he claimed
To have grass in the sack, he looked so ashamed
That Riley wondered, and there on the sack
He'd seen a few feathers from some chicken's back.
At that Mr. Man said, "What the dickens!
So he's the one who's been stealing my chickens!"

And off he took, as also Riley,
Though he slipped along in the woods, right slyly,
Where he could see Brer Fox and his load
And all that happened there on the road.

Mr. Man very soon caught up with him
And asked him why he was looking so grim
And what it was he had in the sack,
And Brer Fox swung it down from his back
And said it was just a great big mass
Of unground Winnianimus grass,
Which some folks thought was good to make
Something they called Whipmewhopme cake.
Then Mr. Man said he'd like to see
What Winnianimus grass could be.

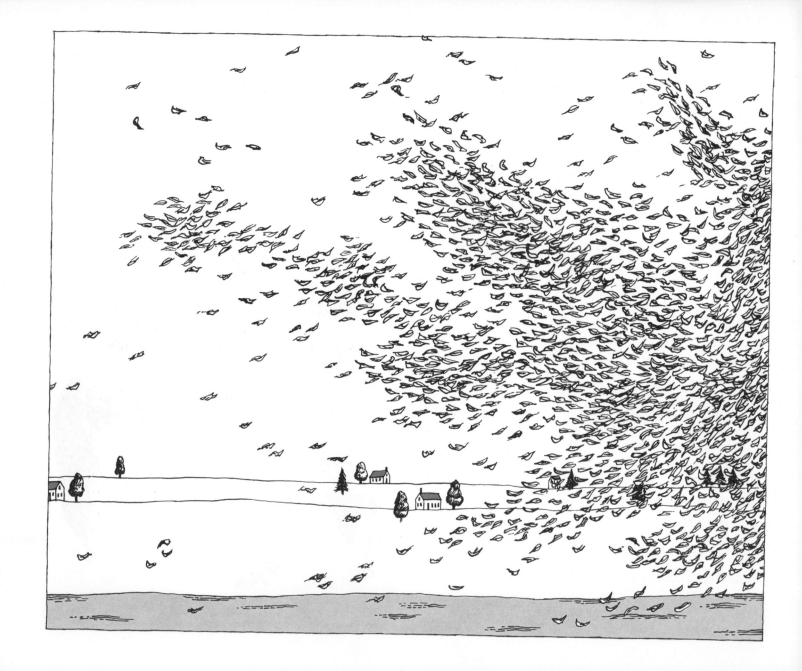

So he opened the bag, and right up in his face
Feathers flew out all over the place,
Whereat Mr. Man grabbed Brer Fox's collar
And made him whoop and made him holler.
He said, "I'll whipmewhopme you!"
And so he did, until he was through.

And Brer Rabbit laughed as hard as he could,
For he indeed very well understood
What old Brer Fox had hoped so highly
To do with the bag he had gotten from Riley.
Then too, Brer Rabbit was ticklish, you know—
So ticklish that now he laughed "Ho! Ho!"
For all of an hour and maybe a half.
'Most anything would make Riley laugh.